Niffs and Whiffs

Niffs and Whiffs

Compiled by Jennifer Curry
Illustrated by Susie Jenkin-Pearce

RED FOX

A Red Fox Book

Published by Random House Children's Books
20 Vauxhall Bridge Road, London SW1V 2SA

A division of Random House UK Ltd

London Melbourne Sydney Auckland
Johannesburg and agencies throughout the world

First published by The Bodley Head Children's Books 1991

Red Fox edition 1992
Reprinted 1992

Printed and bound in Great Britain by
Cox & Wyman Ltd, Reading, Berkshire

ISBN 0 09 984610 1

*This book is dedicated, with thanks,
to all the TRACKER DOG POETS of
Britain who joined me in my search.*

CONTENTS

Tracker Dog Poets

Jennifer Curry wrote,
'Send us a poem,
on Smells. . . .'

All over the world
poets like Bloodhounds sniffed
and tried to catch
the track of a verse –

In Sudan the heat danced
and the words shrivelled,

In France a string of garlic
kept the poem at bay,

In the U.S. of A. the poet inhaled
but the poem jogged off round the block,

The Romanian poet smelt freedom,
sat back and put down her pen.

South American men
cut down slender images,

In the Arctic the poet's nose
froze. . . .

All round Britain poets
sniffed like tracker dogs,
hot on the scent
of a memory that smelt.

A few were dealt
a lucky deal.
They sniffed deep
and found something real
that lay asleep.

Pie Corbett

The Truth about the Abominable Footprint

The Yeti's a Beast
Who lives in the East
  And suffers a lot from B.O.
His hot hairy feet
Stink out the street
  So he cools them off in the snow.

Michael Baldwin

My Dog Smells

My dog smells
the faint scent of
cats to chase.

Her nose twinkles
like a black star,
when it's chicken
on Sunday.

She reads the garden
breeze like a child
with a first comic;
empty-looking air
is full of information,
messages incoming as
she fills her lungs.

And when, in the woods,
she finds where
foxes have been,
she rolls, and then . . .
my dog smells!

Robin Mellor

The Bloodhound

I am the dog world's best detective.
My sleuthing nose is so effective
I sniff the guilty at a distance
And then they lead a doomed existence.
My well-known record for convictions
Has earned me lots of maledictions
From those whose trail of crime I scented
And sent to prison, unlamented.
Folks either must avoid temptation
Or face my nasal accusation.

Edward Anthony

The Nose

My Uncle Bert
Can smell a rat
At fifty paces,
Which is nothing
To be sniffed at.

People get up his nose –
He's on his third postie,
And the rent collector
Hasn't been seen for months.

My Uncle Bert
Doesn't have many friends,
But one thing he does have:
It's the biggest hooter
For miles.

Trevor Harvey

Grandad

Grandad smelled of fish boiled in milk
And liquorice root on which he continually chewed,
Grumbling about taking pills.
Although they were all that kept him alive.

There was a pile of pipe cleaners
By the fireplace
Smelling of dust
And used too many times,

Like the bleached chicken bones
On the bird table.

He had been working on the allotment
In his better trousers,
So they got muddy
And he had scrubbed at them
With a wire brush,
Then had to try and darn them again.

The hardened globule of denture cream
Looked like bird's splash
On the side of the vase,
In which flowers melted into the water,
Staining the glass at the water line.

When I was very small
There was always a toy phone
On which we played a game
In which he ordered sacks of potatoes . . .
So I used to bring them round
Out of the garage.
He gave me 5 pence per sack.

Then he died,
Mixing with smells
Of camomile tea
And boiled fish.

Edward Line (13 years)

Superstink

Big bus at the bus stop.
Ready to go again.
Big noise.
Big cloud of

Robert Froman

The Tar-Boiler

Black, battered and sticky, and smoking blue fumes
All day the tar-boiler has stood in our street,
And the lucky workmen with their rakes and their brooms
Pull and push the thick shiny stuff this way and that.

It squats and it hisses, as though holding its breath,
While under its belly the red furnace roars;
Then, slowly, in gulps from its hot black mouth,
When the foreman opens it, the thick liquid pours.

All day we have stood and drunk the smell down
Like cigarette smoke – but nicer by far,
It's as heavy as something in which you could drown,
So rich and satisfying, the reek of the tar.

We could never grow tired of it; we agree, all ten,
That when we grow up we'll be tar-boilermen.

Brian Lee

from: Rushden Feast, Northants
circa 1948–59

'Feast's come,' we'd whisper in class,
'Ayya gooing down Rec?'
After school we'd cycle to the park,
Fling our bikes on the wet grass,
And ogle the fairground men,
Envious of their exciting world
Of generators, thumping in the midst
Of shining caravans and snaking cables.
We sniffed the smell of axle grease and oil
Mingled with dank, disturbed earth,
And sappy grass
Crushed by huge machines.
In Wellington boots, I tightly held my mother,
Squelching through the mud.
'It allus rains come Feast Week.'

Anita Marie Sackett

Think of Tree

Under
the car smell

over
the tar smell

a sweet green and far smell
flows
down the street.

And it says
drifting by,
    'Think of tree.
    Think of sky.
    Think of ripe apples
    and hay, sun-dry.'

Then you know –
not far away
they are cutting grass
in the park today.

Lilian Moore

The Lavender Field

The mauve colour of the field,
Makes me come and dance.
With the sunset behind
The green, green trees glisten
As the wind whistles through the lavender.
As it is cut down
With a scythe, all of Norfolk smells.

Jenefer Leach (9 years)

Washing Lines

Grandmother said,
'I don't believe that any sheet
Could ever smell as fresh and sweet
As those dried on the garden line,
All flapping white in God's sunshine.'
Grandmother said.

Grandma told me,
When she was small; of wash-house days;
Of misted windows; steam and haze;
The coal-fired copper boiling there;
The hot and soapy-smelling air.
Grandma told me.

In my Mum's house;
An automatic white machine;
Clothes, churning, through a port-hole seen.

And never draped around a fire!
Just rolling in the tumble-drier.
In my Mum's house.

On holiday;
Gran's landing cupboard next to me
Holds cotton sheets which I can see
On slatted shelves, all folded there,
In laundered piles, (Gran says) 'to air.'
On holiday.

My Gran's old bed
Has big soft pillows edged with lace.
The sheets feel kind upon my face;
So fresh; so cool: I could declare
I'm breathing in her garden air.
In Gran's old bed.

                              Robert Sparrow

Sunday Visits

I was a child straight-faced and plain and solemn,
But loving much, and greatly needing love.
My teacher-mother, too busy or too tired
To touch and hold, my father weighted
Down with men's affairs, committees, clubs,
Had little time to know or note my need.

But one there was in my small world
Whose dumpling arms stretched out, enfolded, tucked
Me tight and safe on her child-welcome lap.
And as she reached, and wrapped, and held me close
Against the down-soft pillow of her breasts,
My nose breathed in the fragrant waft and warmth
Of peppermint breath, and wool, and Lifebuoy soap,
And sweat and skin – the long-remembered smell
Of Sunday visits, and my Grandma's love.

Jenny Craig

This Newly Created World

Pleasant it looked,
this newly created world.
Along the entire length and breadth
of the earth, our grandmother,
extended the green reflection
of her covering
and the escaping odours
were pleasant to inhale.

Anon, Winnebago Indian

Summer

Summer smells like . . .
Pot pourri and the bunches of daisies
Peeping out of the rich grass,
Green with goodness.
It fills your lungs and makes you gasp.
And the dog puts his nose into the breeze
And closes his eyes.
The warm smell of rabbits alerts him.
He races, transformed into a greyhound.
You can't stop him now.
I run after him.
He stops, puts his nose into the silent breeze . .
Suddenly, a burst of energy
And he leaps into action!
I can't see him anywhere.
Suddenly two ears pop out of the field,
Where wild flowers grow.
He is running, barking,
Sniffing the fragrance that flows out of them.

Justin Bloomfield (12 years)

My Dog

Max is beautiful and fluffy.
His soft fur is brown and black.
His paws and teeth are sharp.
At night his eyes shine up in the dark.

In the morning, Max waggles his tail.
He's glad that we're up.
When the dark clouds let go their water,
He gets wet and smells like rain.

Michelle Fellows (7 years)

Fish and Chips

Hear the sizzle,
Taste the salt,
See the shiny peas!
Smell the sauce and vinegar –
Fish and chips? Yes please!

Judith Nicholls

Jack-Next-Door

Jack-next-door
    has
bright blue eyes
rosy red cheeks
a great big smile
    BUT –
he smells of fish.

Jack-next-door
    sells
haddock cod and hake
coley trout and skate
mussels shrimps and eels
    SO –
he smells of fish.

Jack-next-door
    has built
a sauna and a shower
whirlpool-bath and pool
jacuzzi wave-machine
    BUT STILL
he smells of fish.

O.K. by me (though not by him)
I LIKE the smell of fish.

Jenny Craig

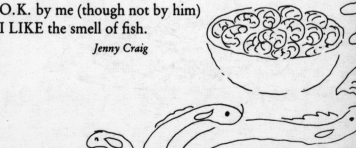

The Old Fellow

There was an old fellow
who lived by the sea
crying, 'O sir! There's no one
so happy as me!
For when in, sir, and out, sir,
the ocean it goes
I have always the sand, sir,
to tickle my toes!'

This cheery old fellow
who lived by the beach
would say over and over:
'It's easy to teach!
For when out, sir, and in, sir,
the ocean it flows,
one has always the salt, sir,
to sniff up one's nose!'

Jean Kenward

Cow Pâté

The cow pat landed,
Settling in outflowing rings,
Rich, steaming, smelling of her.
She turns and tongues a mouth of grass,
Then follows
the pats
on
down
the
lane.

Rona M. Campbell

The Cowpat Throwing Contest

Malc and me and Ian Grey, we couldn't believe
when we heard someone say, that in cattle towns
of the old Wild West, they held cowpat throwing contests!

How awful, how dreadful, what if it hit
you smack in the mouth, you'd gag, you'd be sick,
but we knew, even then, the day would come when we'd
    try it.

And it wasn't very long after that when the three of us
were sent away, 'Get out of the house,
get out of my sight, go somewhere else and play.'

And we walked until the houses stopped, looked
over a hedge and there in a field were pancakes of
the very stuff we'd been talking about for days.

The cows looked friendly so we started up
with a chunk or two that might have been mud
but we knew we'd move on to the slimy stuff before long.

Malc was the first to try it out and scooped up
a really terrible lump, but while Ian was yelling
and backing away, he tripped and sat down in the dung.

Malc was laughing fit to burst and he must have forgotten
his hands were full till he dropped the lot
all down his trousers, then wiped his hands on his shirt.

I made the mistake of grinning too till Malc hit my jacket
and Ian my shoes, and I watched it spreading everywhere,
while the cows just stood there and mooed!

Well after that it was in our hair and down our jumpers
and everywhere. Our finger nails were full of the stuff,
then Ian said, 'Pax, I've had enough.'

'We look awful,' Malc said, 'and we smell as sweet as
a sewage farm in the midday heat, we shouldn't have
     done it,
we've been really daft,' but again Ian started to laugh.

We laughed up the lane while a cloud of flies
trailed us back to Ian's place, where his Mum's grim face
soon shut us up, as she fixed her hose to the tap.

'It's history Mum, it's really true, it's what they did
in the Wild West. . . .', but we lost the rest of what he said
as a jet of water pounded his chest.

Then water was turned on Malc and me, and we both
     went home

in Ian's clothes, while his Mum phoned ours and tried
to explain just what it was that we'd done.

I knew my Mum would have a fit, 'That was it,'
she said, 'The final straw. No way you're going out
to play for a week, no, a month, maybe more.

'Get in that bath, use plenty of soap, how could you act
such a silly dope. Use the nailbrush too and wash
your hair, I'll be in there later to check.'

I scrubbed and I brushed but I couldn't make the smell
disappear, and I wondered how the cowboys coped
when their contest was done and everyone climbed in
    the tub.

And kids held their noses and called out, 'Pooh!'
for days and weeks and months after that, but it didn't
    matter,
we'd proved we were best, not at spellings or sport
or something like that, but at cowpat throwing contests.

Brian Moses

Farmyard Chatter

There they are, every day without fail.
Leather breath and graciously plodding,
The local gossips.
Listen to them whisper, listen as they trip
Over the caked ground.
Fresh straw . . . smelling like that
Box of Weetabix I opened last week.
Sizzling silage in large grey tanks.
Hear it bubble, then splurt against the cold tin.
Breathe in,
And your lungs will fill with roasting dung
And fresh cut grass.
I passed through that farm;
The smells pierced the back of my throat.
And those graciously plodding local gossips
Whispered and stared.

Emma Buckingham (12 years)

Apples and Pears

In grandfather's orchard that long, sunny day,
I smelt apples and pears,
clustered in dark, loaded trees,
or, picked all ready at first light,
lying warm and comfortable in huge baskets,
the old milking shed drenched with their sweetness.
And, from time to time, struck out at wasps

33

moving in their black and yellow squadrons
from the thick blackberry hedges,
to dive greedily into the scattered heaps of gashed fruit
towered, here and there, upon the grass for the pigs'
   delight;
it was a day of ripeness and plundering.

And now, the mists rising, lights on at tea-time,
the fierce raiders dead in their legions,
chilled by the breath of first frosts,
I can still smell grandfather's orchard,
the dense perfume of August's ripeness
as I look at apples and pears from other places,
piled high in mother's best fruit dish,
here, now on the seventh floor of our city flat,
and not a single tree flowering and fruiting below.

Leonard Clark

The Bee's Last Journey to the Rose

I came first through the warm grass
Humming with Spring,
And now swim through the evening's
Soft sunlight gone cold.
I'm old in this green ocean,
Going a final time to the rose.

North Wind, until I reach it,
Keep your icy breath away
That changes pollen into dust.
Let me be drunk on this scent a final time.
Then blow if you must.

Brian Patten

Nosegay

Violets, daffodils,
　　roses and thorn
were all in the garden
　　before you were born.

Daffodils, violets,
　　red and white roses
your grandchildren's children
　　will hold to their noses.

Elizabeth Coatsworth

Digging

Today I think
Only with scents, – scents dead leaves yield,
And bracken, and wild carrot's seed,
And the square mustard field;

Odours that rise
When the spade wounds the roots of tree,
Rose, currant, raspberry, or goutweed,
Rhubarb or celery;

The smoke's smell, too,
Flowing from where a bonfire burns
The dead, the waste, the dangerous,
And all to sweetness turns.

It is enough
To smell, to crumble the dark earth,
While the robin sings over again
Sad songs of Autumn mirth.

Edward Thomas

Burning

The match was struck,
It snatched its prey,
And slowly the paper
Began to curl and scorch.
The corner crumbled away,
As the flame rushed on
Devouring the pure white paper.

It danced and ran, twisting
And turning, then leaping high
In the air.
The hungry flame raced
Onwards.
Leaving red-flecked ash
Slowly drifting downwards.
Now nothing was left but a
Whisp of smoke and a
Faint lingering smell in the air.

Suzy Gilmour (11 years)

A Lady Who Lived in Low Fell . . .

A lady who lived in Low Fell
Asked her friends, 'Is that gas we can smell?'
A large match she struck
And the whole building shook,
Then down in a heap it all fell.

Anon.

Sweet Chestnuts

How still the woods were! Not a redbreast whistled
To mark the end of a mild autumn day.
Under the trees the chestnut-cases lay,
Looking like small green hedgehogs softly bristled.

Plumply they lay, each with its fruit packed tight;
For when we rolled them gently with our feet,
The outer shells burst wide apart and split,
Showing the chestnuts brown and creamy-white.

Quickly we kindled a bright fire of wood,
And placed them in the ashes. There we sat,
Listening how all our chestnuts popped and spat.
And then, the smell how rich, the taste how good!

John Walsh

The Apple's Song

Tap me with your finger,
rub me with your sleeve,
hold me, sniff me, peel me
curling round and round
till I burst out white and cold
from my tight red coat
and tingle in your palm
as if I'd melt and breathe
a living pomander
waiting for the minute
of joy when you lift me
to your mouth and crush me
and in taste and fragrance
I race through your head
in my dizzy dissolve.

I sit in the bowl
in my cool corner
and watch you as you pass
smoothing your apron.
Are you thirsty yet?
My eyes are shining.

Edwin Morgan

Don't Leave the Spoon in the Syrup

The lid was off,
the spoon was in,
the syrup smelled deliciously;
I looked,
I watched,
I sniffed,
and then –
I licked it syrupticiously!

N. M. Bodecker

Cheese Please

When
my
nose
smells
cheese on the breeze,
It
will
simply
sneeze with a please.
AAAAAAAAAAAATCHEDDAR!

Ian Souter

Cabbage – Yuck!

There is a smell that I abhor.
I loathe this odour more and more.
The stink of cabbage on the boil
Makes all the other GOOD smells spoil.
It percolates about the house –
The stench is worse than rotting mouse!

Timothy Sherwood

Going for Greens

I'll be a vegetarian,
I'll start off right away.
I'll give up meat and I'll just eat
Green veggies every day.

I'll have as vegetarian
Baked beans on toasted bread;
Hot oven chips and chocolate whips
And honey thickly spread.

And as a vegetarian,
I'll try out other things:
Fresh peanuts roasted; cheese that's toasted;
Fried battered apple rings.

But really, vegetarians
Need great dedication,

Like eating greens and swedes and beans.
Else: it's starvation!

To be a vegetarian
Must be really tough;
Living off cheese, oats, beans and peas,
And all that sort of stuff.

Being a vegetarian
Sharpens your sense of smell.
Hardly trying; *know* what's frying,
HOT BACON! I can tell!

Being a vegetarian
Is hard work, don't you know.
With bacon sizzling, fried and frizzling;
That *smell* from down below!

I'll be a vegetarian
As soon as I feel able.
Just now I'm late; I'll grab my plate
And sit down at the table.

Robert Sparrow

Papa Moses Killed a Skunk

Papa Moses killed a skunk
Mama Moses cooked the skunk
Baby Moses ate the skunk
My oh my oh how they stunk.

Traditional American rhyme

Safari Smells

The man on the corner
Near Mr Magoo
Has told both my parents he's starting a zoo.
While he named all the creatures he wanted to keep
My mum screwed her nose up a bit like a sheep.
My dad said quite calmly
And what of the smell?
The man looked dumbfounded
The odour – yes well,
The rhino is house trained
The lion's quite clean
And most of the penguins . . . they'll live in the stream.
So if by some offchance there is a bouquet
Let's all hope the wind isn't blowing our way.

John Reid

Giraffe

At the zoo I saw: a long-necked, velvety Giraffe
Whose small head, high above the strawy,
   zoo-y smells
Seemed to be dreaming.
Was she dreaming of African jungles
   and African plains
That she would never see again?

Carson McCullers

Smells

Why is it that the poets tell
So little of the sense of smell?
These are the odours I love well:

The smell of coffee freshly ground;
Or rich plum pudding, holly crowned;
Or onions fried and deeply browned.

The fragrance of a fumy pipe;
The smell of apples, newly ripe;
And printers' ink on leaden type.

Woods by moonlight in September
Breathe most sweet; and I remember
Many a smoky camp-fire ember.

Camphor, turpentine, and tea,
The balsam of a Christmas tree,
These are whiffs of gramarye . . .
A SHIP SMELLS BEST OF ALL TO ME!

Christopher Morley

gramarye – magic

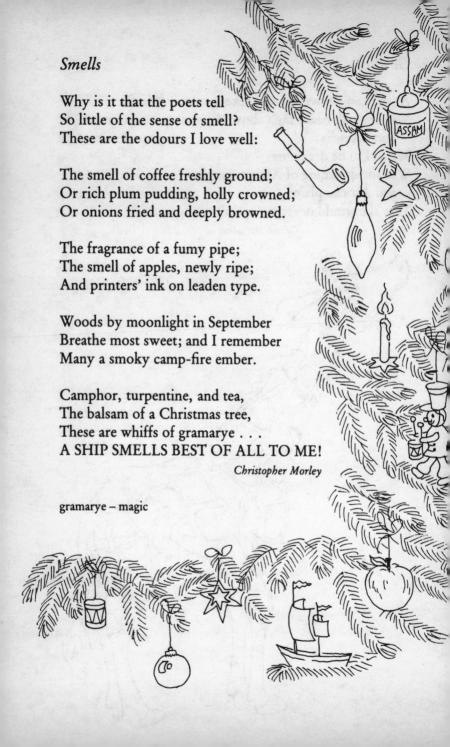

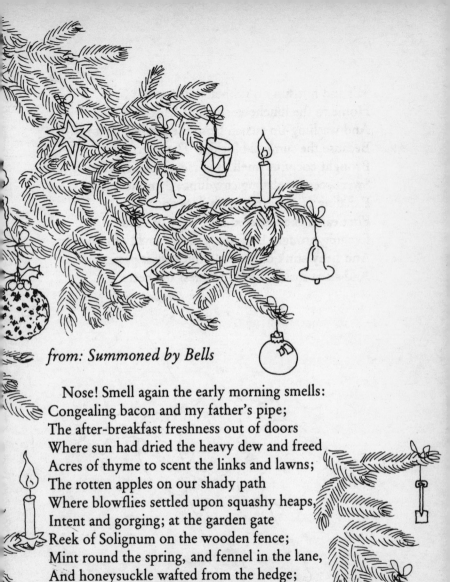

from: Summoned by Bells

Nose! Smell again the early morning smells:
Congealing bacon and my father's pipe;
The after-breakfast freshness out of doors
Where sun had dried the heavy dew and freed
Acres of thyme to scent the links and lawns;
The rotten apples on our shady path
Where blowflies settled upon squashy heaps,
Intent and gorging; at the garden gate
Reek of Solignum on the wooden fence;
Mint round the spring, and fennel in the lane,
And honeysuckle wafted from the hedge;
The Lynams' cess-pool like a body-blow;
Then, clean, medicinal and cold – the sea.
'Breathe in the ozone, John. It's iodine.'
But which is iodine and which is drains?

Salt and hot sun on rubber water-wings . . .
Home to the luncheon smell of Irish stew
And washing-up stench from the kitchen sink
Because the sump is blocked. The afternoons
Brought coconut smell of gorse; at Mably's farm
Sweet scent of drying cowdung; then the moist
Exhaling of the earth in Shilla woods –
First earth encountered after days of sand.
Evening brought back the gummy smell of toys
And fishy stink of glue and Stickphast paste,
And sleep inside the laundriness of sheets.

John Betjeman

The Friday Night Smell

I love the
friday night
smell of
mammie baking
bread – creeping
up to me in
bed, and though
zzzz I'll fall
asleep, before I
even get a
bite – when
morning come,
you can bet
I'll meet a
kitchen table
laden with
bread, still
warm and fresh
salt bread
sweet bread
crisp and brown
& best of all
coconut buns
THAT'S why
I love the
friday night
smell of mammie
baking bread
putting me to
sleep, dreaming
of jumping from

the highest branch
of the jamoon tree
into the red water
creek
beating calton
run & catching
the biggest fish
in the world
plus, getting
the answers right
to every single
sum
that every day
in my dream
begins and ends
with the friday
night smell of
mammie baking
bread, and
coconut buns
of course.

Marc Matthews

from: A Taste of France

France. I say your name
and a thousand scents and smells
enter my memory by the front door
like familiar relatives arriving for a visit:
    a breakfast table set –
the whiff of freshly baked baguettes
mingles with the sugary smell
of chocolate-filled croissants.
The aroma of strong coffee, dark as tree bark,
wafts and drifts temptingly.

John Rice

There Was a Young Lady from Wareham . . .

There was a young lady from Wareham
Whose friends wouldn't let her go near 'em.
She cried, 'Do I smell?'
They answered her, 'Well,
It's your fags, love, we really can't bear 'em!'

Anon.

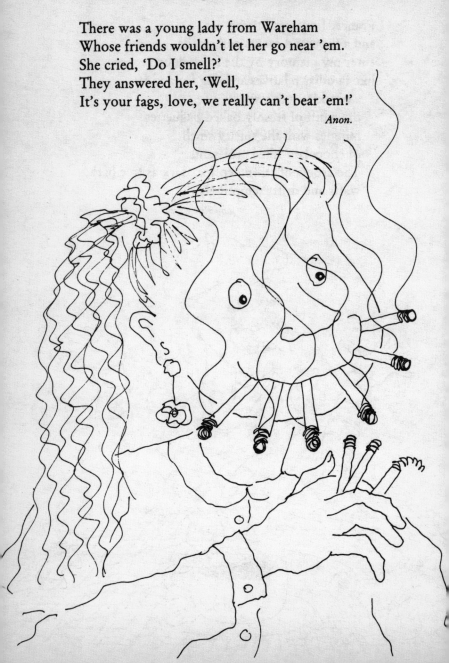

Kisses

I don't like kissing Grandad,
He always seems so prickly,
And I don't like kissing babies much,
They're always wet and sickly.
And I don't like kissing aunties
Who've got powder on their cheek,
And I really hate those people
Who kiss you as you speak.
I don't like kissing uncles,
'Cos they always smell of beer.
I don't mind people who've got colds
'Cos they say, 'Don't come near.'
Daddy always smells of smoke,
But he's better than the rest.
But of all the people in the world,
I like kissing Mummy best.
Sometimes when she's kissed me,
I lick it all away,
Then swallow it and keep it
To have another day.

Rod Hull

There Was an Old Girl of Hong Kong . . .

There was an old girl of Hong Kong
Whose breath was uncommonly strong,
She said, 'I find onions
Are good for my bunions,
So I nibble 'em all the day long.'

Anon.

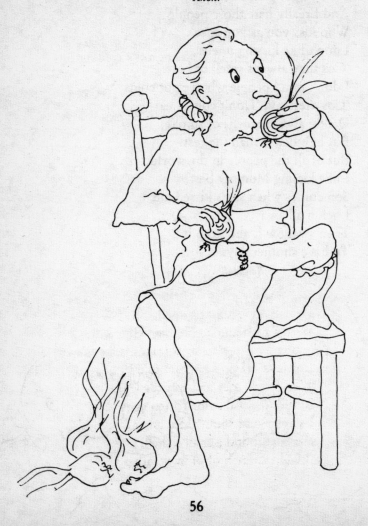

Ghost Hunt

Long after midnight
I searched for the haunted house,
but I didn't see
a speck of a spectre,
nor a fraction of a phantom,
nor a spot of a spook,
nor a pinch of a poltergeist.
I didn't even catch
the sweet scent of a skelington's wellingtons!

Long after midnight
I searched for the haunted house,
but when I couldn't find it
– I gave up the ghost.

John Rice

The Spell of a Witch

I am making a magic spell,
With a toad and a goblin's yell
A phantom's scream, a dragon's feather,
It smells as good as good as ever.
With frog's toes and lizard's legs,
I think I'll add some rotten eggs.
I scream and shout, I moan and yell,
I've just found a snail's shell.
I'll add a pinch of dirty weather,

With a poison dragon's feather.
I stir my brew, I stir my brew,
Some for me and some for you.
Spooky, spooky dark and damp,
I met a wizard I met a tramp.
The wizard gave me a puppy dog's tail,
The tramp gave me a toad and a snail.
I stir my brew, I stir my brew,
Some for me and some for you.
I'll add some poison I'll add some blood,
I think it smells rather good.

Gillian Parker (9 years)

Fee-fi-fo-fum!

Fee-fi-fo-fum!
I smell the blood of an Englishman:
Be he alive or be he dead,
I'll grind his bones to make my bread.

Nursery Rhyme

Fee-fi-fo-hum!

Fee-fi-fo-hum!
I smell the pong of an Englishman.
Be he alive or be he dead,
I wish he were somewhere else instead.

Colin McNaughton

Winding up Smiffy

Calling Smith a smelly git
Only served to get me hit.
But seeing my remark had stung,
I refused to hold my tongue
And announced that his perfume
Was like an old sock in a changing room.
Smith, a little more impressed,
Beat a tattoo upon my chest.

'Take that,' cried Smith. I had no choice
And took it, but I found my voice:
'I say,' I said, 'Do watch it, Smiffy.
Exertion makes you mega-whiffy.'
Steam issued forth from Smiffy's ears:
He'd not been so wound up for years.
Reference to his aroma
Nearly put him in a coma.
I needed one more brilliant phrase
To send him raving mad for days.
And just as I was losing hope
One slipped into my mind like soap:
'You're a malodorous olfaction!'

Now I have both my legs in traction.

Ian Whybrow

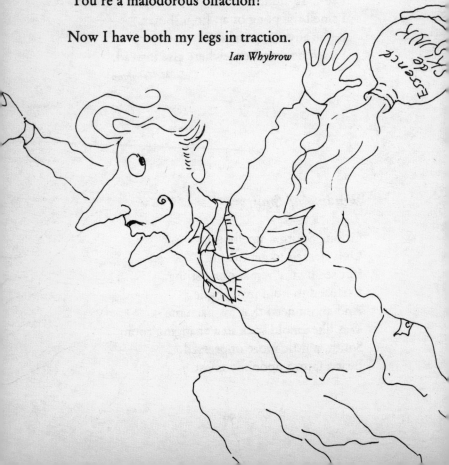

The Bottle of Perfume that Willie Sent . . .

The bottle of perfume that Willie sent
Was highly displeasing to Millicent;
Her thanks were so cold,
They quarrelled, I'm told,
Through that silly scent Willy sent Millicent.

Anon.

*There are more ways of beating a bully than biffing
   him one*

Trevor was a bully, everyone knew,
he had flying fists and if one of them flew
in your direction, you'd know it alright,
he'd feint with his left and jab with his right.

He called kids names which upset them as well
and his favourite taunt was to say, YOU SMELL –

of horse manure and mouldy cheese
of unwashed socks and leftover peas,
You smell, in fact you really stink,
you smell like a yeti, you're the missing link!

Then Gavin decided, with his friend Malc,
to teach Trev a lesson and a can of talc
was opened and poured over Trevor's head,
and we listened amazed as Gavin said

YOU SMELL, in fact you really reek,
you won't need a bath until next week,
you stink of perfume sprays and soap,
of flowers and scented envelopes.

Well Trevor, Malc said, you smell really sweet,
what a gorgeous pong as you stroll down the street.
Then Trevor let out an enormous yell
and everyone scattered, racing pell-mell

We have other ways, I heard Malc call,
to beat a bully and we'll try them all
testing them out one by one on you,
not talc next time, but cold brown stew!

Brian Moses

Uncle Barney's Scrambled Goat

The smell that I adore the most
Is scrambled eggs on buttered toast.
It's hardly Paris or the Ritz
Where eggs are always served with frites.
Still, every mouthful tastes so good
I never think about my pud.

The smell that somehow jams my throat
Is Uncle Barney's billy goat,
An odour that I'm glad to say
Lives nearly forty miles away.
I only hope that in my time
These two smells will not combine.

John Reid

Grey Squirrel

The grey squirrel is sharp
On the move.
He smells of the inside of a tree
Woody.

Peter Gregory (13 years)

In a Field of Clover by the River Charles

The day
was grey
and full of cloud,
the clover
smelled of honey,
and even when
the rain began
that made the day
seem sunny.

N. M. Bodecker

Waiter! This Soup has a Smell . . .

Waiter! This soup has a smell
Reminiscent of brimstone from hell.
　　The taste is as foul
　　As a decomposed owl,
And it looks like the slime on a well.

Anon.

The Florist

Florist shops are beautiful,
All damply green and dimly cool,
And the men who keep them are sure to be
A little baggy about the knee,
With voices pleasant and rather low
From living alone with things that grow;
For you can't stay noisy and hurried where
Petal on petal fills the air
With spiciness, and every tree
Is hung with gayest greenery.
Grocers bustle and butchers shout,
Tradesmen tramp noisily in and out,
But florists are quiet men and kind,
With a sort of fragrance of the mind.

Rachel Field

The Boot and Shoe Man

He lived
With the smell of leather
In the background of his life.
As a lad
Passed busy factories
Stacked outside with sacks
Of leather dust and scraps.
Passed throngs of factory workers
Programmed, by the daily hooter.
The thudding presses
Stamped the shape and pattern
Of his future.
He loved the life of shoes,
Lived and worked for the firm.
Knew a shoe from upper to sole,
Inside and out.
See a shoe, he'd pick it up,
Feel the grain, sniff the leather
And remark on its style and design.
Only dealt with quality shoes!
Not cheap plastic from abroad.
Leather,
Real leather.
'Lets the feet breathe.
These'll last you a lifetime,
Polish 'em well
And they'll not let you down.
Lovely smell.
Leather!'

Anita Marie Sackett

New Shoes

The new shoes sit boxed together
in the comfort of soft crumpled tissue-paper.
Left matching right, right partnering left.
Both open-mouthed,
tongues popping out, laces dropping in.
Two thick moulded frames,
stitched and shaped in strong browned skins
from which escapes,
a rich dark breath of polished leather.
A smoky seasoned smell
that seeps into the top of my head
and creeps all the way down
to the tip of my expectant toes.

Ian Souter

There Was a Young Man from New Delhi . . .

There was a young man from New Delhi
Who kept all his cash in a welly,
But whoever he paid
Always said, 'I'm afraid
I can't take it. Your money's too smelly.'

Miles Kington

Deodorant

Why do they write on the side of deodorants
'FOR UNDERARM FRESHNESS' – Why 'underarm'?
What's the matter with
'Armpit'?
I mean most of us have got
at least one of them,
They are
NORMAL.
'UNDERARM FRESHNESS'.
It makes it sound
like little boys playing cricket.

What I've never figured out about deodorants
though
is where does all the underarm sweat go
once you've blocked up your armpits?
Where does it come out?
Your eyes?
You got sweaty eyes?

You know,
One day they're going to invent a nose deodorant.
Not to stop you being able to smell
to stop – yes –
bogies.
Imagine it.
Up in the morning, into the bathroom
and a quick psssht psssht up your nose.
FOR NO-BOGIE FRESHNESS.
No no no
they couldn't call it bogies.

They'd have to call it
something like
'That unwelcome little business'.

In fact, there are probably people at this very moment
slaving away in research laboratories
over bunsen burners and test tubes
trying to invent deodorants for anything that
doesn't fit into decent life as it is known.

And there'll be people going around spraying deodorants
all over their bodies
and
on their brains.
Brain deodorant
FOR UNDERSKULL FRESHNESS
Stops your brain smelling.
The police would be issued with it.
Here is the News:
As from tomorrow the police
will be equipped with Disinfectant Water Cannon
and Brain Deodorant.

Mike Rosen

Goodbye

Goodbye to my blanket,
I loved how it stank! It
Was snotty and slimy
And Mum said 'It's time he
Got rid of it, burnt it.'
But I cried 'I want it,
It's cosy, it's snuggly,
Who cares if it's ugly,
Its unique aroma
Reminds me of home. Ah
Blanket, ah blanket,
You're soggy and dank yet
I love every piece of you,
All the smeared grease of you,
All the dried spittle
From when I was little –
It's part of my life now,
We're like husband and wife now!'
Then I met Albert
And now he's my pal, but
He doesn't like gungy
Old blankets all spongy
And sickly and pongy.
He says it's all wrong, he
Says I should grow up,
He says I should BLOW up
My blanket, forget it;
To a well-mannered Ted it
Seems utterly nasty,
A part of my past he
Would like to see vanish

So I'm going to be mannish
And grown-up and seven,
Send blanket to heaven.
I'm sorry to lose it
But I really must choose. It
Is Albert or blanket
So now I must thank it
(Dear blanket) for keeping –
While waking and sleeping –
Me snug, wipe the tear from my eye
And say 'Blanket, goodbye!'

John Mole

Putting My Foot In It!

Last Sunday my dad tarmacked our path
and before he went out he told me NOT
to go outside or there would be trouble.
So I went outside.
And there lay the path all black and shiny
like a gigantic strip of wet liquorice.
But it didn't smell like wet liquorice.
No it smelt – DISGUSTING!
The fumes climbed into my nose
and almost blew my nostrils off!
Anyway the path looked finished
so without thinking I set off across it.
But about halfway over I somehow got stuck.
The tarmac path had become a tarmac swamp.
It was sucking at my feet like black glue
I was suck-stuck.
The only way out was to yank hard
and split-slit my trainers.
Eventually I squelched to the end
leaving my footmarks printed on the path
like some mystery from a horror movie.
'The Creature from the Black Swamp!'
Five minutes later inside the house
mum shot out from her bedroom
with her nose sniffing
like a bloodhound on the loose.
'What's that awful smell?'
'Er tar mum. Dad's being tarmacking the path.'
Suddenly her eyes jumped past me,
her face looked like it would stop a clock
and a scream leaped from her mouth.

'AAAAAAAAAAGGGGGHHHHH!'
My eyeballs hit the roof of my head
and then bounced up and down
as if they were on springs.
My attention was definitely nailed to mum's mouth
as she screeched, 'MY CARPET!'
I looked behind me and then swallowed heavily.
The carpet had been decorated with fat lumps of tar
from the sole of MY trainers.
But just as mum was about to rip me in half
her face turned ice-cream white
and disappeared back into her bedroom.
You see she can't stand the smell of tar.
It makes her really ill!
Later when dad came home he was so mad
that he not only went through the roof
but up into outer space as well.
My trouble is I just don't think before I act
and I just end up PUTTING MY FOOT IN IT!

Ian Souter

Smellyvision

Have you heard of Smellyvision?
It's like television,
Except *as well* as sight and sound,
Different smells abound.

What fun!
Imagine – we switch on
'Gardening Time' on BBC 2
And not only can we hear and view
A programme on roses –
But we find the smells go right up our noses!

A million people, I bet,
Would sit by a smellyvision set
To sample the experts talking of blooms
Which emitted aromas right into their rooms,
But I suppose there'd be rather fewer
When those gardening experts got on to manure.

Colin West

The Smelly Mess

We've just spent a day at the local gymkhana,
With barrow, bucket and spade,
Cleaning up all the mess,
That hundreds of horses have made.
But what shall we do with the fruits of our labour?
The odour is hardly divine.
We're going to spread it all over the rhubarb.
I'd rather have custard on mine.

Mark Hamlett (11 years)

Night Noises

My brother's made a nasty noise
So we know very well
That, pretty soon, we're sure to have
A rather nasty smell. . . .

Will it be
The beans for tea,
The curry from last night,
Or the rhubarb pie?
It's certain we
Shall soon find out, all right!

Dive under blankets,
Don't breathe deep,
Just pray we'll quickly
Go to sleep. . . .

Ah.
The rhubarb.

Right – if that's the way you want it!
My turn next . . .
O.K.?

Trevor Harvey

There Was a Young Man of Cornell . . .

There was a young man of Cornell
Who said, 'I'm aware of a smell,
But whether it's drains
Or human remains
I'm really unable to tell.'

Anon.

Stink Bomb

I am malice,
A rotten yolk
Spinning in a glass egg,
One of three potent sisters,
You can call me Fun.

I can clear a classroom
Quicker than trailed-in dog's muck,
Quicker than sick
Piled in the aisle.

In my green eye winks a warning
Of worse humiliations:
For I am no more an accident
Or a symptom of illness
Than my friends the whoopie cushion
And the itching powder.

I put the guff in guffaw,
The camel with its green spit
Has sweeter breath than my last laugh.
Smash me under your heel
And I'll raise the biggest stink since Hitler.

Ian Whybrow

A Chemistry Student from Gillingham . . .

A chemistry student from Gillingham
Kept emptying jam jars and filling 'em
With a poisonous jelly
That was bright green and smelly
So he used it on teachers for killing 'em.

John Rice

Smells

The smell of old chicken wire
wafts out as I open the shed door.
I step inside.
Decomposed leaves and rotting wood
mingle with the scent of cut grass.
I remember the first time I raked the grass,
the handle bobbing up and down
as I pulled it along,
the grass flying up into the air.
I remember the smell of rotting wood.
I was helping dad tear down the shed.
Fungi dust filled the air as I levered out a plank
and dark yellow wood crumbled as I picked it up,
woodlice scrambling out.
They ran and disappeared.
I open the seed drawer.
The smell of decomposed leaves drifts out.
I remember sweeping the path in autumn,
leaves rustling in front of the broom.
I put the leaves in a box,
ready to be burnt.
They burn as I shut the drawer.

Paul Neale (13 years)

A Storehouse of Smells

How does a dozy, dried up smell
contain
a coloured memory?
Maybe we label
little bottles in the brain
to save old smells from going dry.

'Paraffin' still turns me cold,
waking in the winter with a kettle singing on a smoky flame
and bacon burning.
Another bottle, shiny gold
like brocade curtains, with the name
of 'Marmalade', smells of a spring morning.

Next to that, and coloured green,
come all the good smells summer made,
picnics in a field of 'Hay',
'Warm Skin', 'New Bread' and 'Cheddar Cheese',
green 'Apples' mixed with 'Lemonade'
and 'Grass', just mown on Saturday.

Unwelcome smells, like 'Bandages', have blue bottles,
blue for poison, starchy uniforms
I can't avoid in dentists' waiting rooms
or, even as a visitor, in hospitals.
And there are other scary ones,
like 'Roller Towels', that lurk in smelly changing rooms.

How does a dozy, dried up smell
undo
your bottled tears?

A forest path we knew so well,
where 'Violets' and 'Mushrooms' grew,
I could not walk, because it smelt of death, for years.

I almost lost 'Wet Dog', 'Wet Sheep',
Mum's 'Hair', Dad's 'Pipe' and, yes, the camping 'Loo'.
'Pine Trees' and 'River Mud' still make my old heart ache,
while 'Babies' Heads' and 'Cows' can send me off to sleep.
But any ill is cured by 'Seaweed' with a mountain view,
fresh 'Figs' or 'Snow' with 'Chocolate Cake'.

Will you remember how
you filled and labelled every bottle, while the smells
    were new,
and stored your multi-coloured memories of NOW,
each one of them containing little bits of YOU?

Jane Whittle

Words That Make Us Laugh

Now one of the worst is 'Nelly',
another that's bad is 'belly',
but the King of them all is –
SMELLY!

Pie Corbett

INDEX OF CONTRIBUTORS

INDEX OF FIRST LINES

ACKNOWLEDGEMENTS

The editors and publishers would like to thank the following for permission to use copyright material in this collection. The publishers have made every effort to contact the copyright holders but there are a few cases where it has not been possible to do so. We would be grateful to hear from anyone who can enable us to contact them so that the omission can be corrected at the first opportunity.

Andre Deutsch Ltd for 'Deodorant' by Michael Rosen from his *When Did You Last Wash Your Feet?*

Edward Anthony for 'The Bloodhound' from *The Beaver Book of Animal Verse*, edited by Raymond Wilson.

Michael Baldwin for 'The Truth about the Abominable Footprint'.

Catherine Beston Barnes for 'Nosegay' by Elizabeth Coatsworth.

Justin Bloomfield for 'Summer', Halesworth Middle School.

Emma Buckingham for 'Farmyard Chatter', Silver Medal Winner in Cadbury's National Exhibition of Art – Poetry Section, 1990.

Cadbury's National Exhibition of Children's Art – Poetry Section for 'The Lavender Field' by Jenefer Leach, 'Burning' by Suzy Gilmour and 'The Spell of a Witch' by Gillian Parker. All poems appear in the Cadbury's Book of Children's Poetry, Volumes 1–7, published by Century Hutchinson Ltd.

Rona Campbell for 'Cow Pâté' from her *The Hedge*, pub. by Counter-Point Publications, 1988.

Carcanet Press for 'The Apple's Song' by Edwin Morgan from his *Collected Poems*, 1990.

The Literary Executor of Leonard Clark for 'Apples and Pears' by Leonard Clark from *The Singing Time*, pub. Hodder & Stoughton.

Pie Corbett for his 'Tracker Dog Poets' and 'Words That Make Us Laugh'.

Jennifer Curry for 'Sunday Visits' and 'Jack-Next-Door' by Jenny Craig.

Faber and Faber Ltd for 'Don't Leave the Spoon in the Syrup' and 'In a Field of Clover by the River Charles' by N. M. Bodecker from his *Snowman Sniffles*.

Michelle Fellow for 'My Dog', from *I Met a Cat and He was Magic*, published by Cambridge Schools Poetry.

Robert Froman for 'Superstink' from his *Street Poems*, copyright 1971.

Mark Hamlett for 'The Smelly Mess' from *Imagine*, published by Kent Reading & Language Development Centre.

Timothy Sherwood for 'Cabbage – Yuk!'.

Ian Souter for 'Cheese Please', 'New Shoes' and 'Putting My Foot In It!'.

Robert A. Sparrow for 'Washing Lines' and 'Going for Greens'.

Walker Books Ltd for 'Fee-fi-fo-hum!' taken from *There's An Awful Lot Of Weirdos In Our Neighbourhood*. © 1987 Colin McNaughton. First published in the UK by Walker Books Limited.

Mrs A. M. Walsh for 'Sweet Chestnuts' from *The Roundabout by the Sea* by John Walsh.

Colin West for 'Smellyvision'.

Jane Whittle for 'A Storehouse of Smells'.

Ian Whybrow for 'Winding Up Smiffy' and 'Stink Bomb'.

Other great reads ⤴ *from* **Red Fox**

Further Red Fox titles that you might enjoy reading are listed on the following pages. They are available in bookshops or they can be ordered directly from us.

If you would like to order books, please send this form and the money due to:

ARROW BOOKS, BOOKSERVICE BY POST, PO BOX 29, DOUGLAS, ISLE OF MAN, BRITISH ISLES. Please enclose a cheque or postal order made out to Arrow Books Ltd for the amount due, plus 30p per book for postage and packing to a maximum of £3.00, both for orders within the UK. For customers outside the UK, please allow 35p per book.

NAME _____

ADDRESS _____

_____

Please print clearly.

Whilst every effort is made to keep prices low, it is sometimes necessary to increase cover prices at short notice. If you are ordering books by post, to save delay it is advisable to phone to confirm the correct price. The number to ring is THE SALES DEPARTMENT 071 (if outside London) 973 9700.

Other great reads from **Red Fox**

Discover the Red Fox poetry collections

CADBURY'S NINTH BOOK OF CHILDREN'S POETRY
Poems by children aged 4–16.
ISBN 0 09 983450 2   £4.99

THE COMPLETE SCHOOL VERSE
ed. Jennifer Curry
Two books in one all about school.
ISBN 0 09 991790 4   £2.99

MY NAME, MY POEM ed. Jennifer Curry
Find *your* name in this book.
ISBN 0 09 948030 1   £1.95

MONSTROSITIES Charles Fuge
Grim, gruesome poems about monsters.
ISBN 0 09 967330 4   £3.50

LOVE SHOUTS AND WHISPERS Vernon Scannell
Read about all sorts of love in this book.
ISBN 0 09 973950 X   £2.99

CATERPILLAR STEW Gavin Ewart
A collection describing all sorts of unusual animals.
ISBN 0 09 967280 4   £2.50

HYSTERICALLY HISTORICAL Gordon Snell and Wendy Shea
Madcap rhymes from olden times
ISBN 0 09 972160 0   £2.99

Other great reads *from* **Red Fox**

THE SNIFF STORIES Ian Whybrow

Things just keep happening to Ben Moore. It's dead hard avoiding disaster when you've got to keep your street cred with your mates *and* cope with a family of oddballs at the same time. There's his appalling 2½ year old sister, his scatty parents who are into healthy eating and animal rights and, worse than all of these, there's Sniff! If only Ben could just get on with his scientific experiments and his attempt at a world beating *Swampbeast* score . . . but there's no chance of that while chaos is just around the corner.

ISBN 0 09 975040 6   £2.99

J.B. SUPERSLEUTH Joan Davenport

James Bond is a small thirteen-year-old with spots and spectacles. But with a name like that, how can he help being a supersleuth?

It all started when James and 'Polly' (Paul) Perkins spotted a teacher's stolen car. After that, more and more mysteries needed solving. With the case of the Arabian prince, the Murdered Model, the Bonfire Night Murder and the Lost Umbrella, JB's reputation at Moorside Comprehensive soars.

But some of the cases aren't quite what they seem . . .

ISBN 0 09 971780 8   £2.99

Other great reads from Red Fox

Discover the exciting and hilarious books of Hazel Townson!

THE MOVING STATUE

One windy day in the middle of his paper round, Jason Riddle is blown against the town's war memorial statue.

But the statue moves its foot! Can this be true?

ISBN 0 09 973370 6 £1.99

ONE GREEN BOTTLE

Tim Evans has invented a fantasic new board game called REDUNDO. But after he leaves it at his local toy shop it disappears! Could Mr Snyder, the wily toy shop owner have stolen the game to develop it for himself? Tim and his friend Doggo decide to take drastic action and with the help of a mysterious green bottle, plan a Reign of Terror.

ISBN 0 09 935490 X £2.25

THE SPECKLED PANIC

When Kip buys Venger's Speckled Truthpaste instead of toothpaste, funny things start happening. But they get out of control when the headmaster eats some by mistake. What terrible truths will he tell the parents on speech day?

ISBN 0 09 956810 1 £2.25

THE CHOKING PERIL

In this sequel to *The Speckled Panic*, Herbie, Kip and Arthur Venger the inventor attempt to reform Grumpton's litterbugs.

ISBN 0 09 950530 4 £2.25